TRY NOT TO LAUGH CHALLENGE™

WOULD YOU RATHER?

EASTER
EDITION

An Easter-Themed Interactive and Family Friendly Question Game for
Boys, Girls, Kids and Teens

Try Not To Laugh Challenge
BONUS PLAY

Join our Joke Club and get the Bonus Play PDF!

Simply send us an email to:

TNTLPublishing@gmail.com

and you will get the following:

- 10 Hilarious Would You Rather Questions
- An entry in our Monthly Giveaway of a $50 Amazon Gift card!

We draw a new winner each month and will contact you via email!

Good luck!

Welcome to
The Try Not to Laugh Challenge
Would You Rather?
EASTER EDITION

RULES:

• Face your opponent and decide who is 'Player 1' and 'Player 2'.

• Starting with 'Player 1', read the Would You Rather question aloud and pick an answer. The same player will then explain why they chose that answer in the most hilarious or wacky way possible!

• If the reason makes 'Player 2' laugh, then a laugh point is scored!

• Take turns going back and forth, then mark your total laugh points at the end of each round!

• Whoever gets the most laugh points is officially crowned the 'Laugh Master'!

• If ending with a tie, finish with the Tie-Breaker round for WINNER TAKES ALL!

Most importantly, have fun and be SILLY!

REMEMBER, these scenarios listed in the book are solely for fun and games! Please do <u>NOT</u> attempt any of the crazy scenarios in this book.

ROUND

9

Player ①

(DON'T FORGET TO EXPLAIN YOUR ANSWERS!)

Would you rather have an Easter food fight with your family OR have an all-day Easter dance-a-thon contest?

Laugh Point_____ /1

Would you rather be chased by a pack of turtles swinging Twizzler swords OR tickled by the whiskers of a sneezing rabbit?

Laugh Point_____ /1

Player ❶

(DON'T FORGET TO EXPLAIN YOUR ANSWERS!)

Would you rather live on a pirate ship made out of sticky jelly beans OR on a jet plane made entirely of marshmallows?

Laugh Point_____/1

Would you rather eat a 100-year-old Easter candy bar OR your grandma's famous fruitcake?

Laugh Point_____/1

Pass the book to Player 2 ⟶

Player 2

Would you rather be a bunny whose giant ears always drag on the ground OR a tiny dog whose legs are 3-feet long?

Laugh Point_____ /1

Would you rather make people fall in love, like Cupid OR deliver candy and hide eggs, like the Easter Bunny?

Laugh Point_____ /1

Player ②

Would you rather catch your Easter candy jamming out in their own jug band, causing them to explode with shock, OR discover your kitchen utensils perform yoga in the drawer and are all permanently bent out of shape?

Laugh Point_____ /1

Would you rather live inside the game, Candy Land OR live inside the movie, 'Jumanji'?

Laugh Point_____ /1

Time to add up your points! ⟶

Add up your scores and record them below!

Player ⬛**1**

/4
ROUND TOTAL

Player ⬛**2**

/4
ROUND TOTAL

ROUND CHAMPION

ROUND

2

Player 1

(DON'T FORGET TO EXPLAIN YOUR ANSWERS!)

Would you rather ride the wildest, highest-hopping bunny OR the fastest spinning Tazmanian devil?

Laugh Point_____/1

Would you rather have to herd 50 rabbits into a tiny farmhouse OR have to catch 3 super bouncy kangaroos in the desert?

Laugh Point_____/1

Player 1

(DON'T FORGET TO EXPLAIN YOUR ANSWERS!)

Would you rather forever be missing your 2 front teeth OR have 2 giant front teeth like a rabbit?

Laugh Point_____ /1

Would you rather the Easter Bunny have wings and deliver your Easter basket like a stork OR the Easter Bunny lay eggs like a chicken on top of your bed?

Laugh Point_____ /1

Pass the book to Player 2 ⟶

Player

(DON'T FORGET TO EXPLAIN YOUR ANSWERS!)

Would you rather swim under a soda waterfall OR in a swimming pool full of milkshakes?

Laugh Point____ /1

Would you rather only get Reese's peanut butter cups in your Easter basket OR only get Cadbury creme eggs?

Laugh Point____ /1

Player

(DON'T FORGET TO EXPLAIN YOUR ANSWERS!)

Would you rather be trapped in an Easter Bunny suit OR doomed to roam the halls of your school in a chicken suit?

Laugh Point_____ /1

Would you rather have the song 'Here Comes Peter Cottontail' OR the song 'Little Bunny Foo Foo' stuck in your head for two weeks?

Laugh Point_____ /1

Time to add up your points! ⟶

Add up your scores and record them below!

Player **1**

___/4
ROUND TOTAL

Player **2**

___/4
ROUND TOTAL

___
ROUND CHAMPION

ROUND

3

Player 1

(DON'T FORGET TO EXPLAIN YOUR ANSWERS!)

Would you rather have an army of minions, but they never listen to you OR have a pet dragon, but all it wants to do is sleep?

Laugh Point_____/1

Would you rather be a bunny with extra-long front teeth OR a chicken with rainbow feathers?

Laugh Point_____/1

Player ❶

Would you rather go to a dentist who always uses hot cinnamon-flavored toothpaste on you, OR go to a doctor who always spits on you when he talks?

Laugh Point_____ /1

◆

Would you rather kiss a slimy frog OR lick a hairy camel's face?

Laugh Point_____ /1

Pass the book to Player 2 ⟶

Player 2

Would you rather spend a week inside the movie 'Peter Rabbit', and cause mayhem with the furry rabbit family OR a week stuck in 'Zootopia' and be a cop with Judy Hopps?

Laugh Point_____ /1

Would you rather have a pet chicken that barks like a dog OR a duck that roars like a lion?

Laugh Point_____ /1

Player ②

(DON'T FORGET TO EXPLAIN YOUR ANSWERS!)

Would you rather eat 5 large chocolate Easter eggs OR 20 small deviled eggs, as fast as you can?

Laugh Point____ /1

Would you rather inherit the Coca-Cola factory, but never get to drink any of it OR inherit Willy Wonka's factory, but never get to eat any of the sweets?

Laugh Point____ /1

Time to add up your points! ⟶

Add up your scores and record them below!

Player 1　　　　 /4
ROUND TOTAL

Player 2　　　　 /4
ROUND TOTAL

ROUND CHAMPION

ROUND

4

Player ❶

(DON'T FORGET TO EXPLAIN YOUR ANSWERS!)

Would you rather walk around with mustard on your head for a day OR spend a day with ketchup in your socks?

Laugh Point_____/1

Would you rather write with hands like the Hulk OR talk on the phone while wearing vampire teeth?

Laugh Point_____/1

28

Player 1

(DON'T FORGET TO EXPLAIN YOUR ANSWERS!)

Would you rather spend all day wearing your dad's hot, sweaty work clothes OR go to the mall with your underwear over your shorts for 3 hours?

Laugh Point_____/1

Would you rather wear a swimsuit outside during the frozen winter OR wear a giant Easter egg costume to the beach during summer?

Laugh Point_____/1

Pass the book to Player 2 ⟶

Player ②

(DON'T FORGET TO EXPLAIN YOUR ANSWERS!)

Would you rather own a magic genie bottle OR own a magic flying carpet?

Laugh Point____/1

Would you rather be able to hide Easter eggs with the speed of Superman OR find the eggs using Superman's ability to see through walls?

Laugh Point____/1

Player 2

(DON'T FORGET TO EXPLAIN YOUR ANSWERS!)

Would you rather have to carry your Easter basket on your back wherever you go OR carry every individual Easter egg 10 miles to your home, like an ant?

Laugh Point_____/1

Would you rather live in a treehouse full of noisy chipmunks OR a nest with angry geese?

Laugh Point_____/1

Time to add up your points! ⟶

Add up your scores and record them below!

Player **1**

/4

ROUND TOTAL

Player **2**

/4

ROUND TOTAL

ROUND CHAMPION

ROUND

5

33

Player 1

(DON'T FORGET TO EXPLAIN YOUR ANSWERS!)

Would you rather have an endless Easter, but never get to hunt Easter eggs OR endless Christmas, but never get to open stockings?

Laugh Point_____ /1

Would you rather have a pet rabbit that breathes fire, like a dragon OR a pet hamster that can grow as big as a dinosaur?

Laugh Point_____ /1

Player ①

Would you rather have to wear a funny umbrella hat OR scuba fins, every time it rains?

Laugh Point_____/1

Would you rather lightning strike close by every time you take a bite of Easter candy OR thunder rumble every time you find an Easter egg?

Laugh Point_____/1

Pass the book to Player 2 ⟶

Player ②

Would you rather be responsible for dropping a jelly bean in an hourglass, every minute for a week OR for making sure each Easter cookie has exactly the same amount of sugar crystals?

Laugh Point____ /1

Would you rather live forever as an baby chick OR live 9 lives as an unlucky Halloween cat?

Laugh Point____ /1

Player 2

(DON'T FORGET TO EXPLAIN YOUR ANSWERS!)

Would you rather play the egg spoon toss with a slime-filled Easter egg OR dodgeball with rotten milk-filled water balloons?

Laugh Point____ /1

Would you rather jump on the moon with your alien BFF OR explore the Pyramids with your mummy BFF?

Laugh Point____ /1

Time to add up your points! →

Add up your scores and record them below!

Player **1**   **/4**
ROUND TOTAL

Player **2**   **/4**
ROUND TOTAL

ROUND CHAMPION

ROUND

6

Player ①

Would you rather go to the pool wearing an Easter Bunny costume OR wearing a full body T-Rex suit?

Laugh Point____ /1

Would you rather live in the world of Minecraft OR get to visit Mario's world every weekend?

Laugh Point____ /1

Player ❶

(DON'T FORGET TO EXPLAIN YOUR ANSWERS!)

Would you rather every time you drop something it turns into hundreds of Skittles OR every time you touch something it turns into a half-melted chocolate bar?

Laugh Point_____/1

Would you rather dive into a pile of the stinkiest Easter eggs OR bathe in a giant tub of the stickiest marshmallow fluff?

Laugh Point_____/1

Pass the book to Player 2 ⟶

Player

(DON'T FORGET TO EXPLAIN YOUR ANSWERS!)

Would you rather live on Easter Island with the Easter Bunny OR on Candy Cane Lane with Santa's elves?

Laugh Point____ /1

Would you rather paint your house with a waterhose filled with lime green paint, OR paint each side to look like a different Easter egg?

Laugh Point____ /1

42

Player ②

(DON'T FORGET TO EXPLAIN YOUR ANSWERS!)

Would you rather be an international popstar, but secretly lip-sync OR have an incredible voice, but never get discovered?

Laugh Point_____ /1

Would you rather only eat ice cream for the rest of your life OR only eat Chick-fil-a chicken nuggets for the rest of your life?

Laugh Point_____ /1

Time to add up your points! →

Add up your scores and record them below!

Player 1   /4
_____
ROUND TOTAL

Player 2   /4
_____
ROUND TOTAL

_____
ROUND CHAMPION

ROUND 7

Player 1

(DON'T FORGET TO EXPLAIN YOUR ANSWERS!)

Would you rather ride a backward roller coaster 25x in a row OR go down a 100-foot water slide that lands in a pool of slime, 15x in a row?

Laugh Point____ /1

Would you rather be able to control the weather like Storm from X-Men OR shapeshift like Mystique?

Laugh Point____ /1

Player 1

(DON'T FORGET TO EXPLAIN YOUR ANSWERS!)

Would you rather be able to have super gekko muscles like Gekko from PJ Masks OR have super ninja skills like Night Ninja?

Laugh Point____ /1

Would you rather dive into an Easter egg ball pit OR jump on a series of mini-trampolines for a mile?

Laugh Point____ /1

Pass the book to Player 2 ⟶

Player ②

(DON'T FORGET TO EXPLAIN YOUR ANSWERS!)

Would you rather sing 'Do Your Ears Hang Low' in front of your school while fully clothed OR in front of 100 strangers, while only wearing your underwear?

Laugh Point_____/1

Would you rather only be able to play Fortnite for the rest of your life OR be able to play every other game, but never be able to play Fortnite again?

Laugh Point_____/1

48

Player ❷

Would you rather be able to watch all the TV you want, but never eat chocolate again OR eat anything you want, but never be able to watch TV again?

Laugh Point_____ /1

◆

Would you rather eat a plate of candy corn pancakes OR eat a plate of licorice waffles?

Laugh Point_____ /1

Time to add up your points! ⟶

49

Add up your scores and record them below!

Player 1

/4
_____
ROUND TOTAL

Player 2

/4
_____
ROUND TOTAL

_____
ROUND
CHAMPION

ROUND

Player 1

(DON'T FORGET TO EXPLAIN YOUR ANSWERS!)

Would you rather cook an entire Easter lunch with Spongebob Squarepants OR bake cookies for everyone with Attila, from 'Tangled Ever After'?

Laugh Point____/1

Would you rather your mind be trapped inside the Easter Bunny OR your mind awake, but your body is frozen in ice forever?

Laugh Point____/1

Player ⓵

(DON'T FORGET TO EXPLAIN YOUR ANSWERS!)

Would you rather be a snowman with a carrot nose that the Easter Bunny wants to eat OR would you rather be the Easter Bunny hungry for the snowman's nose?

Laugh Point_____/1

Would you rather be able to breathe underwater and go swimming with the Loch Ness Monster OR breathe in outer space and go exploring different worlds with aliens?

Laugh Point_____/1

Pass the book to Player 2 ⟶

Player ②

Would you rather realize you went to school in only your underwear and a t-shirt OR get locked in your school overnight by mistake?

Laugh Point_____ /1

Would you rather have to hop like a rabbit everywhere you go for a month OR eat like a starving monkey for a week?

Laugh Point_____ /1

Player ②

(DON'T FORGET TO EXPLAIN YOUR ANSWERS!)

Would you rather your ears got HUGE whenever you lie OR your toes fall off temporarily when you exaggerate?

Laugh Point_____ /1

Would you rather trip over your own rabbit feet constantly OR shed hair all over the sofa, like dogs do?

Laugh Point_____ /1

Time to add up your points! →

Add up your scores and record them below!

Player **1**

/4
ROUND TOTAL

Player **2**

/4
ROUND TOTAL

ROUND CHAMPION

ROUND

9

Player 1

Would you rather have a flying car like the Jetsons OR a Mystery Machine like Scooby Doo?

Laugh Point_____ /1

Would you rather have a chicken that lays jelly beans, but you never know if they will be good or yucky flavors, OR have a rabbit that always poops out M&M's?

Laugh Point_____ /1

58

Player 1

(DON'T FORGET TO EXPLAIN YOUR ANSWERS!)

Would you rather everyone in the world speak in backward sentences OR everyone sing what they want to say?

Laugh Point____ /1

Would you rather sleep in a cave with a hundred hyper rabbits OR sleep on a mountain with a family of hungry bears?

Laugh Point____ /1

Pass the book to Player 2 ⟶

Player ❷

Would you rather drink a smoothie made with marshmallows, sprinkles, and hot dogs OR a milkshake made with chocolate, bacon and eggs?

Laugh Point_____/1

Would you rather win the Easter egg hunt and get unlimited candy for the year, OR win and get to pick out any animal as a pet?

Laugh Point_____/1

Player ❷

Would you rather learn to dance the polka with an elderly neighbor OR wear matching bunny suits with your sibling for a day?

Laugh Point____ /1

Would you rather live in a house always stocked with your favorite Easter candy OR a house always stocked with your favorite Christmas snacks?

Laugh Point____ /1

Time to add up your points! →

Add up your scores and record them below!

Player **1**

___/4___
ROUND TOTAL

Player **2**

___/4___
ROUND TOTAL

_____

ROUND CHAMPION

ROUND

10

Player ❶

Would you rather be locked inside a small cage with 25 baby bunnies OR be stuck inside a fenced yard with 25 puppies?

Laugh Point_____/1

Would you rather walk across a tightrope while dressed as the Easter Bunny in front of your entire school, OR dance the 'Funky Chicken' while dressed as a chicken at the first pep rally of the season?

Laugh Point_____/1

Player 1

(DON'T FORGET TO EXPLAIN YOUR ANSWERS!)

Would you rather be a tiny Easter Bunny with giant thumper feet that make you jump super high OR be a 10-foot long dog with 1-inch legs?

Laugh Point_____ /1

Would you rather your main form of transportation be a bike that only goes backward OR travel everywhere through the sewer tunnels?

Laugh Point_____ /1

Pass the book to Player 2 ⟶

Player ❷

(DON'T FORGET TO EXPLAIN YOUR ANSWERS!)

Would you rather have all your teeth fall out every night OR have your eyebrow hairs grow like crazy caterpillars in the beginning of each week?

Laugh Point_____ /1

Would you rather have to take a cold shower every morning OR have to count backward to 200 every night?

Laugh Point_____ /1

Player ❷

(DON'T FORGET TO EXPLAIN YOUR ANSWERS!)

Would you rather be rich and famous, but your only friend is Peter Rabbit OR live a quiet, boring life, but be friends with all your favorite celebrities?

Laugh Point____ /1

Would you rather only eat Peeps OR candy corn, as every snack for the rest of your life?

Laugh Point____ /1

Time to add up your points! ⟶

Add up your scores and record them below!

Player **1**   **/4**
_____
ROUND TOTAL

Player **2**   **/4**
_____
ROUND TOTAL

_____
ROUND CHAMPION

Add up all your points from each round.
The PLAYER with the most points is crowned
The Laugh Master!

In the event of a tie, continue to Round 11
for the Tie-Breaker Round!

Player **1** _____
GRAND TOTAL

Player **2** _____
GRAND TOTAL

_____

The
Laugh Master

ROUND

11

TIE-BREAKER
(WINNER TAKES ALL!)

Player 1

Would you rather live in a tree burrow with Peter Rabbit's family OR live in the Hundred Acre Wood with Rabbit, Tigger and Pooh?

Laugh Point_____ /1

Would you rather find a pirate chest full of Easter candy OR explore a secret cave and find the Easter Bunny's hideout?

Laugh Point_____ /1

Player 1

(DON'T FORGET TO EXPLAIN YOUR ANSWERS!)

Would you rather have the Energizer Bunny for a gym coach OR Bugs Bunny as your math teacher?

Laugh Point_____ /1

Would you rather travel back in time and have dinner with anyone you wish OR meet yourself from 20 years into the future?

Laugh Point_____ /1

Pass the book to Player 2 ⟶

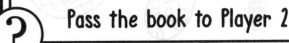

73

Player 2

(DON'T FORGET TO EXPLAIN YOUR ANSWERS!)

Would you rather have to eat 10 chocolate bunnies without using your hands OR have to eat 30 marshmallow Peeps in 5 minutes?

Laugh Point_____ /1

Would you rather poop Easter eggs OR have tears made of hot sauce?

Laugh Point_____ /1

Player ②

Would you rather travel blindfolded through a food maze, and the only way out was to follow the smell of garbage OR travel barefoot through a slime tunnel, and the only way out was to dig a path with your toes?

Laugh Point_____ /1

Would you rather live the rest of your life without chocolate OR without pizza?

Laugh Point_____ /1

Time to add up your points! ⟶

Add up all your points from Round 11.
The PLAYER with the most points is crowned
The Laugh Master!

Player  /4
ROUND TOTAL

Player  /4
ROUND TOTAL

The
Laugh Master

Check out our

 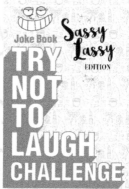 

Visit our Amazon Store at:

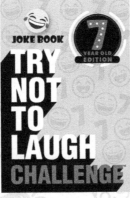

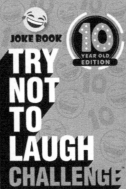

Made in the USA
Middletown, DE
29 March 2020

87463520R00046